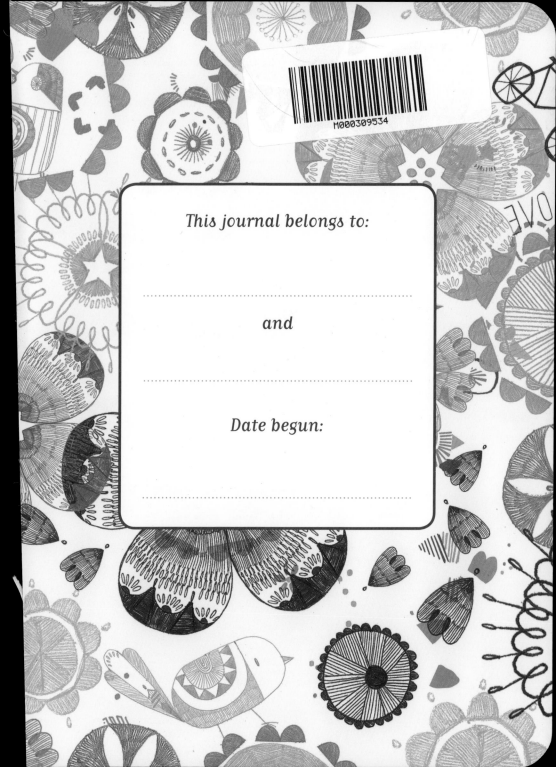

This journal belongs to:

....

and

....

Date begun:

....

Like Mother, Like Daughter

A Discovery Journal for the Two of Us

by Paula Spencer Scott
and Page Spencer

PETER PAUPER PRESS, INC.
WHITE PLAINS, NEW YORK

PETER PAUPER PRESS
Fine Books and Gifts Since 1928

OUR COMPANY

In 1928, at the age of twenty-two, Peter Beilenson began printing books on a small press in the basement of his parents' home in Larchmont, New York. Peter—and later, his wife, Edna—sought to create fine books that sold at "prices even a pauper could afford."

Today, still family owned and operated, Peter Pauper Press continues to honor our founders' legacy of quality, value, and fun for big kids and small kids alike.

Illustrations by Paper and Cloth

Designed by Heather Zschock

Copyright © 2015 Peter Pauper Press, Inc.
202 Mamaroneck Avenue
White Plains, NY 10601

ISBN 978-1-4413-0839-9
Printed in China
7 6 5 4 3 2 1

Visit us at www.peterpauper.com

Like Mother, Like Daughter

A Discovery Journal for the Two of Us

What's inside

Why a mother-daughter journal?

A mother's view...

I'm a big believer in the power of a journal, any journal, a power I've been delighted to pass on to my own three girls.

I was nine when I began my first diary. My aunt introduced me to the idea when she gave me a thick datebook left over from her job as a legal secretary, complete with the title *Lawyer's Handy Book* embossed on the cover. (The first 200 pages contained a phone directory of every lawyer in the city; I doodled mod flowers over them with colored markers when I couldn't think of anything to write.)

The next year I upgraded to an old-fashioned diary with lined pages and a tiny lock. Though the matching tiny key was quickly lost, a lifelong habit had definitely been found.

In the decades since, I've written in all kinds of journals: page-a-day, fill-in-the-blank, lined, unlined, plain notebooks, and ones with colorful, beautiful covers (my favorite).

Like my aunt, I love to give girls diaries, datebooks, and blank books as birthday and Christmas presents. Now all three of my daughters are teenagers. (Yes, you read that right, three teenage girls! Plus three boys in their twenties—lots of moving parts in my life!) All three girls have turned out to be sporadic journal-keepers themselves. It's fitting, in fact, that I wrote this journal together with my youngest, who—because I'm an author—was christened Page, after the pages in a book!

We write for zillions of reasons: To confide and complain, to keep a record of what's happened, to sort out decisions or events, to remember weird dreams or funny comments, to amuse ourselves when we're bored, to say things that are too hard to say out loud. The formats you can write in are just as varied. I like lists as well as full sentences. Random scraps of ideas scrawled down as they pop into your head work, too.

A rant here, a mope or triumph there, and before you know it, history is stuck to the page, like so many well-preserved butterflies. **It's pretty cool, later, to hold a chapter of your life in your hands between two covers.**

A mother-daughter journal is a shared chapter in the story of your lives.

That's especially wonderful at a time when moms' and daughters' stories often seem to be pulling apart. (Is it some kind of cosmic joke that as soon as our girls turn into interesting young women we want to know even better, they discover texting, social media, movies, selfies, hanging out, romance, driving, team sports, and a wide world of other outside attractions?)

Girls have so much to say in the tween/teen years and beyond. It's a time when you're figuring out the rules of life, social systems, this crazy world, and above all, yourself. Your friends are sorting through the same things, but on confusingly different timetables. Daughters are built of smart questions and sharp opinions. Their wit and wisdom make them fun to be around. So does their passion for things they care about. And their deep confusion means they still need you, too, thank goodness!

A journal like this one is neutral territory, a way to talk even when one or both of you is short on time or inclination. (Hey, I'm guilty of a bad mood, too!) Unlike a blog or a social feed, it's private. Unlike a face-to-face conversation, there's no eye contact necessary.

It's also a shortcut to seeing one another as people. Gain insights into one another's likes and dislikes, values and wishes, preferences and pet peeves. As a daughter I would have loved such a sneak-peek into my mom's brain. Now, as a mom, well—same thing!

A mother-daughter journal is, not least, something fun to do together that's just yours (and that's not digital!). If you've never kept a journal before, it's a starter kit for a lifelong habit. Or if one of you already does, it's a natural extension of what you know is a pretty cool thing.

Anyone—any two!—can keep a journal.

Paula Spencer Scott

Why a mother-daughter journal?

A daughter's view....

I used to think a journal was a private thing. Privacy is a core value of mine. Why would you write down your innermost thoughts for someone else to see? Why would you want to share a journal with your *mom*, of all people?!

I only had one idea of what a journal could be.

But then, over many conversations (and a few cupcakes), my mom and I started thinking about what would happen if you could take the best parts of keeping a journal and mix them with the best parts of talking together.

Why do a journal with your mother?

Because we don't always get along with our mothers
You probably love your mom. At the same time, you probably hate your mom too some-times. My mom and I definitely do not always get along well and we do not have the perfect mother-daughter relationship. Even when we're getting along great, it can be hard to get the right words out because we see many things differently or we get impatient with one another. If we're not getting along, I worry about saying the wrong thing that could make a tense situation worse.

In a journal, you can take your time to think things out before you "say" them in writing. I definitely write better than I talk. Through journaling, you can easily interact with one another, in solitude.

Because it's private communication
My multiple—five!—older siblings and I don't get along well sometimes. Being able to rant to my mom about a situation instead of complaining in person (and possibly causing a scene with my siblings, should they overhear) is a perfect solution. You and your mom can learn a lot from each other and it'll only be between you two.

Because you "save" time
I love writing notes to myself and then discovering them months or even years later. You get to reread your past. Not having the best memory, I find this to be very compelling. I used to be afraid that one day, I'd only be able to remember a handful of memories of being younger. By writing down many more "handfuls" in a journal, I know I'll be able to recover more memories.

Because you get to talk to yourself, as well as to each other

On the first day of my English class in my freshman year of high school, we were given the task of writing a letter to ourselves about our goals for the semester and any other thoughts we had. I wrote goals like "improve note-taking during lectures." But I also slipped into journal mode. I described what I was like. I gave advice to my "future self." Then, on the last day of class, the teacher gave the letters back to us. It was very cool to see how I'd changed since the beginning of the semester.

Because you just might start a great habit

My actual journal-keeping started on the last day of sixth grade, which was just about three years ago. Since I would be soon moving to California from North Carolina, I figured I should capture my impressions of the last few weeks of where I'd lived for the majority of my life. Who knew I would fill up several notebooks after that? Now I'm in high school, and I still like to jot down my thoughts in a notebook when something exciting or noteworthy happens.

Because you'll make your mom happy (and yeah, yourself too)

This book is a really good device to connect with your mom, which is cool because nowadays I don't think a lot of kids do that often enough with their parents. Relationships are important—especially with parents—and communication is Number 1 in having a good relationship.

You can learn a lot from your parents when you interact. For instance, while mapping out this journal with my mom, I learned that she can be very stern about work and getting things done! She kept me busy with the project in ways that turned out to be fun.

That's what I hope for you: To use this journal to communicate with your mom, whether things are happy or rocky, and to get to know her better—in a way that, I promise, will turn out to be pretty fun for the both of you!

How to use this journal

This journal is organized into different kinds of writing experiences, from no-thinking-necessary to deep thinking.

The short version: **Use it however you want! Have fun!** *(Page recommends this!)*

But in case you're curious, here's the longer version of our suggestions:

Write a little or a lot.

Some prompts in this book are meant to be light, quick pulse-takers: *What do you think? What do you like? What's your favorite?* . . . Other prompts invite a little more thought. Jot a few lines or squish in a few paragraphs. This kind of journal is a bit like an accordion—it can be as compact or expansive as you choose.

Start at the beginning, or skip around.

This journal lends itself to free-wheeling. You don't have to work through the pages from beginning to end, or in any particular order at all. Find a section you feel like doing right now. Mark the page where you leave off, so the other person can find it and read it before her turn.

Do it together, or separately.

Many parts of this journal can be done in tandem, perfect for vacations or rainy days. For other parts, you might want to take turns. Fill in your part, mark the page, and pass it to the other person so she can write a bit. A turn a day (or every few days) is also a fun, no-stress way to share this book. This is a journal built for trading back and forth.

Talk about it, or not.

Some things in this journal lend themselves to follow-up conversations. "I didn't know you liked that!" you might find one of you saying. Or, "I keep wondering why you said . . ." If you're in the right mood, it can open up some interesting conversation.

But we also know talk doesn't always come easily. It's also just fine if you decide to go by the motto, "What goes in the journal, stays in the journal." Agree that what you write down is for your two pairs of eyes only—not for a "discussion."

Another way: Decide you'll write follow-up questions in the journal and pass your conversation on paper back and forth. There's plenty of room here for that approach, too.

Fill it in all at once, or make it last.

An interactive journal like this is a perfect pack-along for travel, camping, or while on a holiday, where you can fill it in together all in one swoop. Alternately, you can jump right in now. Make it a nightly ritual, for example. Or save it for when things are crazy-busy and you feel a need to slow down and connect. Use it as a touchstone between the two of you.

You could also surprise one another with a turn at the journal, by passing it to and fro at unusual times and in unusual ways. (Saved for sick days? Hidden under a pillow? Set at the table next to the breakfast cereal?)

Enjoy it twice.

So much of what we record these days (via phone snapshots, texts, instant messages) is here and now, here and gone. What you write down in a journal, though, is something you can hang on to. It's something you can have a good time with twice: when you write in it now, and when you revisit it.

Write down the date you start journaling in the front of the book so you'll remember. Years from now one or both of you can pull it out and crack up (or say, "Awwww!").

Ready, set, go!

nothing like holding a fresh, empty new journal
in your hands and wondering what will wind up in there—
nothing, that is, except getting started!

Likes

Name and compare your
favorites and "besties!"

How well do we REALLY know each other?

Fill this out and compare!

	Mother	Daughter
BASIC FAVORITES		
Color:		
Time of day:		
Day of the week:		
Month of the year:		
Season:		
Flower:		
Type of gemstone:		
Kind of pet:		
Dog breed:		
Wild animal:		
Bird:		

Mom's favorite quote:

Daughter's favorite quote:

	Mother	Daughter
MORE FAVORITES		
Piece of clothing:		
T-shirt:		
Scent:		
Kind of weather:		
Store:		
Restaurant:		

Mom's favorite way to spend a rainy day:

Daughter's favorite way to spend a rainy day:

	Mother	Daughter
FAVORITE FOODS		
Breakfast:		
Lunch:		
Dinner:		
Dessert:		
Fruit:		
Berry:		
Veggie:		
Nut:		
Breakfast cereal:		
Cheese:		
Movie-watching snack:		
Cookie:		
Candy:		
Pizza topping(s):		
Ice cream flavor:		
Ice cream topping:		

	Mother	Daughter
MORE FAVORITE FOODS		
Drink on a hot day:		
Drink on a cold day:		
Spice:		
Comfort food:		
Guilty pleasure:		
Celebratory meal:		
Thing to bake:		
Dish to make someone else:		
New foods in the past year:		
Things to order in a restaurant:		

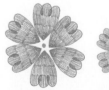

	Mother	Daughter
FAVORITE NAMES AND PEOPLE		
Girls' names:		
Boys' names:		
Dog names:		
Cat names:		
Horse names:		
Mom character in books or movies:		
Girl character in books or movies:		
Author:		
Children's book author:		
Cartoonist:		

	Mother	Daughter
MORE FAVORITES		
Historical figure:		
President:		
Superhero:		
Disney princess:		
FAVORITE ENTERTAINMENT		
Singer:		
Music genre:		
Song:		
Band:		
Radio station:		
Childhood book:		
Recent book:		
Book series:		
Actor:		
Actress:		
Movie genre:		
Comedy movie:		
Scary movie:		

	Mother	Daughter
Romantic movie:		
Action movie:		
TV shows:		
Websites:		
Apps:		
Best 3 movies:		
1.		
2.		
3.		
Best 3 books:		
1.		
2.		
3.		

	Mother	Daughter

**FAVORITE
FUN STUFF**

Childhood toy:

Sports team:

Musical instrument:

Amusement
park ride:

Sport to watch:

Sport to play:

Kind of exercise:

Card game:

Favorite board game:

Mom's favorite way to relax by herself:

Daughter's favorite way to relax by herself:

Mom's favorite way to relax with friends:

Daughter's favorite way to relax with friends:

Mom's favorite way to relax with the family:

Daughter's favorite way to relax with the family:

	Mother	Daughter
FAVORITE PLACES		
Country:		
State:		
City:		
Place to wear a bathing suit:		
Local site:		
Imaginary place (from books, movies, other):		
Room in our house:		
MY BESTS		
Best friend(s):		
1.		
2.		
3.		
My lucky number:		
My lucky charm:		
Best subject in school:		
Most athletic thing I ever did:		

	Mother	Daughter
Best (non-physical) quality about myself:		
Best hair length (me):		
Best hair length (you):		
Kids' movie I never get tired of watching:		
Picture book I'll always love:		
My sports idol:		
My personal hero:		
Businessperson I admire most:		
Gadget I couldn't live without:		
Three women who inspire me:		
1.		
2.		
3.		

Mom's proudest achievement:

....

....

....

Daughter's proudest achievement:

....

....

....

Mom's best dream ever:

....

....

....

Daughter's best dream ever:

....

....

....

Mom's best thing about the weekend:

....

....

....

Daughter's best thing about the weekend:

....

....

....

Best advice Mom has ever given:

....

....

Best advice Daughter has ever given:

....

....

Best advice Mom has ever received:

....

....

Best advice Daughter has ever received:

....

....

Best way to cheer Mom up:

....

Best way to cheer Daughter up:

....

Mom's best thing about being a girl/woman:

....

Daughter's best thing about being a girl/woman:

....

	Mother	*Daughter*
MY FIRSTS		
Pet:		
Trip away from home:		
Sleepover:		
Sport I played:		
Movie I ever saw in a movie theater:		
Friend I remember:		
Celebrity crush:		
Real-life crush:		
State I traveled to (other than my own):		
Plane ride (from where to where?):		
Big purchase:		

First time Mom stood up for herself:

First time Daughter stood up for herself:

First time Mom stood up for someone else:

First time Daughter stood up for someone else:

First time Mom felt proud of herself:

First time Daughter felt proud of herself:

	Mother	Daughter
AND SOME DISLIKES . . .		
Least favorite subject:		
Household chore I hate:		
Least favorite food:		
Worst movie I ever saw:		
Worst book I ever read:		
Worst thing ever eaten:		
Worst haircut ever:		
Habit I wish I could break:		
Habit I wish you could break:		
Habit of MINE you wish I could break:		
Hardest thing about ___ grade:		

Mom's instant mood destroyer:

Daughter's instant mood destroyer:

Most annoying thing my daughter says:

Most annoying thing my mom says:

Thing Mom hates for people to say:

Thing Daughter hates for people to say:

Mom's pet peeve about morning:

Daughter's pet peeve about morning:

Mom's pet peeve about where we live:

Daughter's pet peeve about where we live:

FAQs

Let's play "20 Questions!"

Stuff mothers and daughters wonder about

20 Qs for my mother

1. Do you like your name, or is there a different one you wish you had?

....

....

....

....

2. What were you like in school at my age?

....

....

....

....

3. Tell me 3 things you're afraid of:

....

....

....

4. If you were stuck on a desert island with 3 people, who would you want them to be?

....

....

....

5. If we were the same age (either mine or yours) would we be friends?

6. Who should play YOU in a movie about your life, and what would the movie be called?

7. Who should play ME in a movie about my life, and what would the movie be called?

8. Describe yourself in 3 words:

9. Okay, now describe ME in 3 words:

10. Do you believe in magic? Why/why not?

....

....

....

....

11. What book character do you wish you could be, and why?

....

....

....

....

12. In what ways am I like you?

....

....

....

....

....

....

13. In what ways am I different from you?

....

....

....

14. What causes do you feel strongly about?

....

....

....

15. What does "love" mean to you?

....

....

....

16. What have you done that makes you really proud?

....

....

....

17. Who is the kindest person you know and why?

....

....

....

18. If you could live at any time in history, when would it be, and why?

19. How is being a mom different from what you expected?

20. Is there anything you wish you could ask your parents?

My five bonus questions for you, Mother:

1.

2.

3.

4.

5.

20 Qs for my daughter

1. Do you like your name or is there a different one you wish you had?

2. What subject do you like best in school and why?

3. Name 3 things that worry you:

4. If you were stuck on a desert island with 3 people, who would you want them to be?

5. If we were the same age (either mine or yours) would we be friends?

6. Who should play YOU in a movie about your life, and what would the movie be called?

7. Who should play ME in a movie about my life, and what would the movie be called?

8. Describe yourself in 3 words:

9. Okay, now describe ME in 3 words:

10. Do you believe in fate?

11. What's your dream career?

12. What do I do that embarrasses you?

13. If you had $1,000, what would you spend it on?

....

....

....

14. What household rules would be different if you were in charge?

....

....

....

15. What would you change about yourself?

....

....

....

16. What would you never change about yourself?

....

....

....

17. Do you believe in ghosts?

....

....

....

....

18. If you were an animal, what one would you be and why?

....

....

....

....

19. What social cause do you feel strongly about?

....

....

....

....

20. If a genie gave you only one wish, what would you wish for?

....

....

....

....

My five bonus questions for you, Daughter:

1.

2.

3.

4.

5.

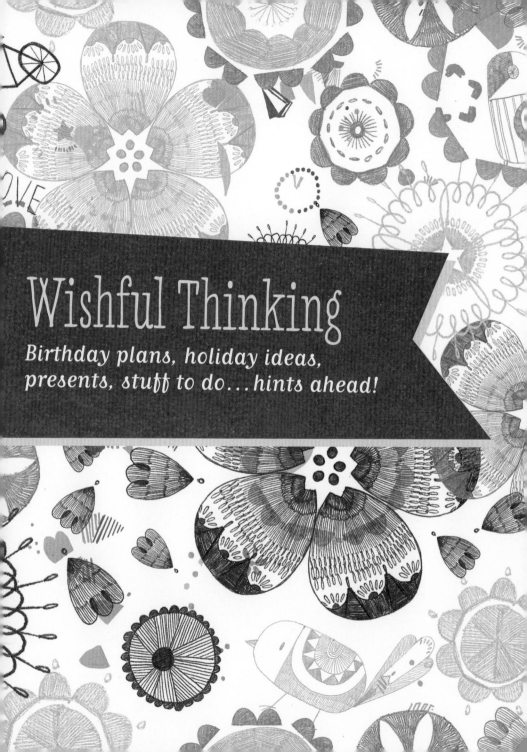

Wishful Thinking

Birthday plans, holiday ideas, presents, stuff to do...hints ahead!

Birthdays

Mother and daughter dream birthday planner

	Mother	Daughter
Place:		
Theme:		
Who's there:		
Food:		
Cake:		
Icing:		
Writing on cake:		
Candles:		
Decorations:		
Time of day:		
Invitations:		
Other details:		

MOTHER *Five birthday gifts I'd loooove*

1.

2.

3.

4.

5.

DAUGHTER *Five birthday gifts I'd loooove*

1.

2.

3.

4.

5.

Please don't even think about getting me this!

Mom:

Daughter:

Holidays

MOTHER, describe your perfect...

Thanksgiving:

Halloween:

Valentine's Day:

New Year's:

Mother's Day:

Christmas / Hanukkah / Kwanzaa / winter holidays you celebrate:

Holiday tradition we should continue:

....

....

....

Holiday tradition I wouldn't miss:

....

....

....

Holiday foods I look forward to all year:

....

....

....

Holiday decorations I hope I have forever:

....

....

....

Seasonal song I look forward to all year:

....

....

....

MOTHER

What are your top 3 favorite holidays, and why?

1.

2.

3.

Which holiday was best for you last year and why?

Which didn't live up to your wishes and why?

If we invented a holiday together:

What would it be called?

What would it celebrate?

When would it occur?

What would we do on this holiday?

Who should celebrate this holiday?

Holidays

DAUGHTER, describe your perfect...

Thanksgiving:

Halloween:

Valentine's Day:

New Year's:

Christmas / Hanukkah / Kwanzaa / winter holidays you celebrate:

Holiday tradition we should continue:

Holiday tradition I wouldn't miss:

Holiday foods I look forward to all year:

Holiday decorations I hope I have forever:

Seasonal song I look forward to all year:

DAUGHTER

What are your top 3 favorite holidays, and why?

1.

2.

3.

Which holiday was best for you last year and why?

Which didn't live up to your wishes and why?

If we invented a holiday together:

What would it be called?

What would it celebrate?

When would it occur?

What would we do on this holiday?

Who should celebrate this holiday?

Travel

Our next family vacation—my top 3 picks:

1.

2.

3.

Collaborate: A dream mother-daughter road trip (just us!)

Where we should go:

When we should go:

How we should get there:

What we should do there:

Audio books we should listen to:

Snacks for the car:

Stuff we can't travel without:

Souvenirs to hunt for:

Pictures to take:

Map, GPS, or go without a plan?

My ultimate dream vacation:

What's great about traveling with you:

What's not-so-great about traveling with you (sorry!):

Some places I've always wanted to drive to:

Some places I've always wanted to fly to:

Travel

Our next family vacation—my top 3 picks:

1. ....

2. ....

3. ....

Collaborate: A dream mother-daughter road trip (just us!)

Where we should go:

When we should go:

How we should get there:

What we should do there:

Audio books we should listen to:

Snacks for the car:

Stuff we can't travel without:

Souvenirs to hunt for:

Pictures to take:

Map, GPS, or go without a plan?

My ultimate dream vacation:

What's great about traveling with you:

What's not-so-great about traveling with you (sorry!):

Some places I've always wanted to drive to:

Some places I've always wanted to fly to:

Life in general

Draw or describe your dream room:

Mother

Daughter

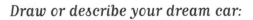

Draw or describe your dream car:

Mother

Daughter

MOTHER

If I had a million dollars, I'd . . .

If I had $100 in my pocket tomorrow, I'd . . .

My wishes for humankind:

My wishes for the planet:

LOVE

DAUGHTER

If I had a million dollars, I'd . . .

If I had $100 in my pocket tomorrow, I'd . . .

My wishes for humankind:

My wishes for the planet:

Our bucket list

Eighteen things we should do together before the big 18th birthday

	Mother	Daughter
1.		
2.		
3.		
4.		
5.		
6.		
7.		
8.		
9.		

Mom's thoughts on how we should celebrate high school graduation:

	Mother	Daughter
10.		
11.		
12.		
13.		
14.		
15.		
16.		
17.		
18.		

Daughter's thoughts on how we should celebrate high school graduation:

Rewind and Fast Forward

Take a peek at each other's past memories and imagined futures.

Looking backward

Mother to daughter

My first impressions of you when you joined our family:

Daughter to mother

My earliest memories of you:

MOTHER

Who was my first best friend? Have I kept in touch?

If I could have one do-over day, it would be the day I . . .

A stand-out day in my memory is . . .

DAUGHTER

Who was my first best friend? Have I kept in touch?

If I could have one do-over day, it would be the day I . . .

A stand-out day in my memory is . . .

MOTHER

If I could live in any historical era I would choose . . .

The historical events that have had a big impact on my life are . . .

Five books I really, really want you to read:

1.

2.

3.

4.

5.

If I could live in any historical era I would choose . . .

The historical events that have had a big impact on my life are . . .

Five childhood toys I really, really want you to save:

1.

2.

3.

4.

5.

MOTHER *The best trip we ever took...*

Where:

When (ages):

Why I loved it:

What I especially remember:

Best souvenir:

DAUGHTER

The best trip we ever took...

Where:

When (ages):

Why I loved it:

What I especially remember:

Best souvenir:

MOTHER

What was my best birthday so far? Why?

A time I felt really alive was:

The saddest I ever remember being was:

What was my best birthday so far? Why?

....

....

....

....

....

A time I felt really alive was:

....

....

....

....

....

The saddest I ever remember being was:

....

....

....

....

....

MOTHER

The best and worst dreams I remember:

....

....

....

....

....

....

....

Something I've done that I've never told you about before:

....

....

....

....

....

....

....

....

DAUGHTER

The best and worst dreams I remember:

Something I've done that I've never told you about before:

Looking forward

Where I see you in 5 years, Daughter:

....

....

....

....

....

....

Where I see me in 5 years:

....

....

....

....

....

Where I see you in 5 years, Mother:

Where I see me in 5 years:

MOTHER

Where I see you in 10 years, Daughter:

Where I see me in 25 years:

Where I see you in 10 years, Mother:

Where I see me in 25 years:

Daughter's future wedding wants

Groom:
....

Attendants:
....

....

....

Big or small wedding:
....

Place:
....

Style:
....

Time of year:
....

Time of day:
....

Reception menu:
....

....

....

Cake:
....

Music:
....

Other details:
....

....

....

Bride's look:

....

....

....

....

Mother-of-the-bride's look:

....

....

....

....

Marrying advice from Mom:

MOTHER

What do you want to do when you grow up. Daughter?

Do you want kids someday, Daughter? If so, how many?

DAUGHTER

When you were my age, Mom, what did you want to do when you grew up?

Did you always know you wanted kids, Mom?

MOTHER

What are 5 things you'd like to do in your lifetime, Daughter?

1.

2.

3.

4.

5.

What are 5 things you'd like me to do in my lifetime?

1.

2.

3.

4.

5.

What are 5 things you'd like to see happen in your lifetime?

1.

2.

3.

4.

5.

DAUGHTER

What are 5 things you'd like to do in your lifetime, Mom?

1.

2.

3.

4.

5.

What are 5 things you'd like me to do in my lifetime?

1.

2.

3.

4.

5.

What are 5 things you'd like to see happen in your lifetime?

1.

2.

3.

4.

5.

Speed Ratings

Quick! Give your gut reactions.

Do together or answer separately and then compare. Count up how many things you have in common—or not!

This or that?

Check the box next to the thing you think is better!

Mother	Daughter
☐ broccoli or Brussels sprouts ☐	☐ broccoli or Brussels sprouts ☐
☐ long skirts or miniskirts ☐	☐ long skirts or miniskirts ☐
☐ big dogs or little dogs ☐	☐ big dogs or little dogs ☐
☐ French braids or ponytails ☐	☐ French braids or ponytails ☐
☐ morning person or night owl ☐	☐ morning person or night owl ☐
☐ print books or e-books ☐	☐ print books or e-books ☐
☐ sweet or sour ☐	☐ sweet or sour ☐
☐ pancakes or waffles ☐	☐ pancakes or waffles ☐
☐ dogs or cats ☐	☐ dogs or cats ☐
☐ tea or coffee ☐	☐ tea or coffee ☐
☐ lotion sunblock or spray sunblock ☐	☐ lotion sunblock or spray sunblock ☐
☐ sunrise or sunset ☐	☐ sunrise or sunset ☐
☐ pen or pencil ☐	☐ pen or pencil ☐
☐ chat online or face-to-face ☐	☐ chat online or face-to-face ☐
☐ dark chocolate or milk chocolate ☐	☐ dark chocolate or milk chocolate ☐
☐ video games or board games ☐	☐ video games or board games ☐
☐ fire or ice ☐	☐ fire or ice ☐

THIS OR THAT?

Mother	Daughter
☐ Coke or Pepsi ☐	☐ Coke or Pepsi ☐
☐ bath or shower ☐	☐ bath or shower ☐
☐ math or English ☐	☐ math or English ☐
☐ silver or gold ☐	☐ silver or gold ☐
☐ tortoise or hare ☐	☐ tortoise or hare ☐
☐ comedy or horror ☐	☐ comedy or horror ☐
☐ chocolate or vanilla ☐	☐ chocolate or vanilla ☐
☐ long hair or short hair ☐	☐ long hair or short hair ☐
☐ big cities or small towns ☐	☐ big cities or small towns ☐
☐ picnic or 5-star restaurant ☐	☐ picnic or 5-star restaurant ☐
☐ fiction or nonfiction ☐	☐ fiction or nonfiction ☐
☐ speak up or keep silent ☐	☐ speak up or keep silent ☐
☐ sit-down restaurant or drive-thru ☐	☐ sit-down restaurant or drive-thru ☐
☐ bar soap or body wash ☐	☐ bar soap or body wash ☐
☐ black ink or colored ink ☐	☐ black ink or colored ink ☐
☐ roller coaster or merry-go-round ☐	☐ roller coaster or merry-go-round ☐
☐ plain or cartoon Band-Aids ☐	☐ plain or cartoon Band-Aids ☐
☐ denim or sequins ☐	☐ denim or sequins ☐

THIS OR THAT?

Mother	Daughter
☐ phone or laptop ☐	☐ phone or laptop ☐
☐ total honesty or little white lies ☐	☐ total honesty or little white lies ☐
☐ popcorn or candy corn ☐	☐ popcorn or candy corn ☐
☐ pink or blue ☐	☐ pink or blue ☐
☐ heels or flats ☐	☐ heels or flats ☐
☐ lakes or oceans ☐	☐ lakes or oceans ☐
☐ teddy bears or dolls ☐	☐ teddy bears or dolls ☐
☐ nutty PB or smooth PB ☐	☐ nutty PB or smooth PB ☐
☐ beach or mountains ☐	☐ beach or mountains ☐
☐ posters or paintings ☐	☐ posters or paintings ☐
☐ cursive or printing ☐	☐ cursive or printing ☐
☐ bikini or one-piece ☐	☐ bikini or one-piece ☐
☐ city mouse or country mouse ☐	☐ city mouse or country mouse ☐
☐ planning or winging it ☐	☐ planning or winging it ☐
☐ hello or good-bye ☐	☐ hello or good-bye ☐
☐ antiques or the next new thing ☐	☐ antiques or the next new thing ☐
☐ flip-flops or sneakers ☐	☐ flip-flops or sneakers ☐
☐ convertible or SUV ☐	☐ convertible or SUV ☐

How many stars?

Daughter first: Circle or fill in the number of stars you think your mom would give the following . . . then let Mom fill in her side and see what she really thinks.

	Daughter's guess	Mother's real answer
Bubble baths	☆ ☆ ☆ ☆ ☆	☆ ☆ ☆ ☆ ☆
A woman president	☆ ☆ ☆ ☆ ☆	☆ ☆ ☆ ☆ ☆
Selfies	☆ ☆ ☆ ☆ ☆	☆ ☆ ☆ ☆ ☆
Bungee jumping	☆ ☆ ☆ ☆ ☆	☆ ☆ ☆ ☆ ☆
Black nail polish	☆ ☆ ☆ ☆ ☆	☆ ☆ ☆ ☆ ☆
Coffee	☆ ☆ ☆ ☆ ☆	☆ ☆ ☆ ☆ ☆
Going out to eat	☆ ☆ ☆ ☆ ☆	☆ ☆ ☆ ☆ ☆
Concerts	☆ ☆ ☆ ☆ ☆	☆ ☆ ☆ ☆ ☆
Baking	☆ ☆ ☆ ☆ ☆	☆ ☆ ☆ ☆ ☆
Vacuuming	☆ ☆ ☆ ☆ ☆	☆ ☆ ☆ ☆ ☆
Dresses	☆ ☆ ☆ ☆ ☆	☆ ☆ ☆ ☆ ☆
Texting	☆ ☆ ☆ ☆ ☆	☆ ☆ ☆ ☆ ☆
Museums	☆ ☆ ☆ ☆ ☆	☆ ☆ ☆ ☆ ☆
Rock music	☆ ☆ ☆ ☆ ☆	☆ ☆ ☆ ☆ ☆
Country music	☆ ☆ ☆ ☆ ☆	☆ ☆ ☆ ☆ ☆
Rap music	☆ ☆ ☆ ☆ ☆	☆ ☆ ☆ ☆ ☆

	Daughter's guess	Mother's real answer
Folk music	☆ ☆ ☆ ☆ ☆	☆ ☆ ☆ ☆ ☆
Hip-hop	☆ ☆ ☆ ☆ ☆	☆ ☆ ☆ ☆ ☆
Classical music	☆ ☆ ☆ ☆ ☆	☆ ☆ ☆ ☆ ☆
Jazz	☆ ☆ ☆ ☆ ☆	☆ ☆ ☆ ☆ ☆
Sleeping in	☆ ☆ ☆ ☆ ☆	☆ ☆ ☆ ☆ ☆
Piercings	☆ ☆ ☆ ☆ ☆	☆ ☆ ☆ ☆ ☆
Rainy weather	☆ ☆ ☆ ☆ ☆	☆ ☆ ☆ ☆ ☆
Watching the World Cup	☆ ☆ ☆ ☆ ☆	☆ ☆ ☆ ☆ ☆
Watching the Olympics	☆ ☆ ☆ ☆ ☆	☆ ☆ ☆ ☆ ☆
Watching reality shows	☆ ☆ ☆ ☆ ☆	☆ ☆ ☆ ☆ ☆
Tattoos	☆ ☆ ☆ ☆ ☆	☆ ☆ ☆ ☆ ☆
White jeans	☆ ☆ ☆ ☆ ☆	☆ ☆ ☆ ☆ ☆
Singing in the shower	☆ ☆ ☆ ☆ ☆	☆ ☆ ☆ ☆ ☆
Singing in public	☆ ☆ ☆ ☆ ☆	☆ ☆ ☆ ☆ ☆
Arguing	☆ ☆ ☆ ☆ ☆	☆ ☆ ☆ ☆ ☆
Bling	☆ ☆ ☆ ☆ ☆	☆ ☆ ☆ ☆ ☆
Veganism	☆ ☆ ☆ ☆ ☆	☆ ☆ ☆ ☆ ☆
Running	☆ ☆ ☆ ☆ ☆	☆ ☆ ☆ ☆ ☆
Unicorns	☆ ☆ ☆ ☆ ☆	☆ ☆ ☆ ☆ ☆

How many stars?

Now mother: Circle or fill in the number of stars you think your daughter would give the following . . . then let her fill in her side and see what she really thinks.

	Mother's guess	Daughter's real answer
Bubble baths	☆ ☆ ☆ ☆	☆ ☆ ☆ ☆
A woman president	☆ ☆ ☆ ☆	☆ ☆ ☆ ☆
Selfies	☆ ☆ ☆ ☆	☆ ☆ ☆ ☆
Bungee jumping	☆ ☆ ☆ ☆	☆ ☆ ☆ ☆
Black nail polish	☆ ☆ ☆ ☆	☆ ☆ ☆ ☆
Coffee	☆ ☆ ☆ ☆	☆ ☆ ☆ ☆
Going out to eat	☆ ☆ ☆ ☆	☆ ☆ ☆ ☆
Concerts	☆ ☆ ☆ ☆	☆ ☆ ☆ ☆
Baking	☆ ☆ ☆ ☆	☆ ☆ ☆ ☆
Vacuuming	☆ ☆ ☆ ☆	☆ ☆ ☆ ☆
Dresses	☆ ☆ ☆ ☆	☆ ☆ ☆ ☆
Texting	☆ ☆ ☆ ☆	☆ ☆ ☆ ☆
Museums	☆ ☆ ☆ ☆	☆ ☆ ☆ ☆
Rock music	☆ ☆ ☆ ☆	☆ ☆ ☆ ☆
Country music	☆ ☆ ☆ ☆	☆ ☆ ☆ ☆
Rap music	☆ ☆ ☆ ☆	☆ ☆ ☆ ☆

	Mother's guess	Daughter's real answer
Folk music	☆ ☆ ☆ ☆ ☆	☆ ☆ ☆ ☆ ☆
Hip-hop	☆ ☆ ☆ ☆ ☆	☆ ☆ ☆ ☆ ☆
Classical music	☆ ☆ ☆ ☆ ☆	☆ ☆ ☆ ☆ ☆
Jazz	☆ ☆ ☆ ☆ ☆	☆ ☆ ☆ ☆ ☆
Sleeping in	☆ ☆ ☆ ☆ ☆	☆ ☆ ☆ ☆ ☆
Piercings	☆ ☆ ☆ ☆ ☆	☆ ☆ ☆ ☆ ☆
Rainy weather	☆ ☆ ☆ ☆ ☆	☆ ☆ ☆ ☆ ☆
Watching the World Cup	☆ ☆ ☆ ☆ ☆	☆ ☆ ☆ ☆ ☆
Watching the Olympics	☆ ☆ ☆ ☆ ☆	☆ ☆ ☆ ☆ ☆
Watching reality shows	☆ ☆ ☆ ☆ ☆	☆ ☆ ☆ ☆ ☆
Tattoos	☆ ☆ ☆ ☆ ☆	☆ ☆ ☆ ☆ ☆
White jeans	☆ ☆ ☆ ☆ ☆	☆ ☆ ☆ ☆ ☆
Singing in the shower	☆ ☆ ☆ ☆ ☆	☆ ☆ ☆ ☆ ☆
Singing in public	☆ ☆ ☆ ☆ ☆	☆ ☆ ☆ ☆ ☆
Arguing	☆ ☆ ☆ ☆ ☆	☆ ☆ ☆ ☆ ☆
Bling	☆ ☆ ☆ ☆ ☆	☆ ☆ ☆ ☆ ☆
Veganism	☆ ☆ ☆ ☆ ☆	☆ ☆ ☆ ☆ ☆
Running	☆ ☆ ☆ ☆ ☆	☆ ☆ ☆ ☆ ☆
Unicorns	☆ ☆ ☆ ☆ ☆	☆ ☆ ☆ ☆ ☆

Story Time 2.0

Different kinds of stories, now that
Mother Goose *is far behind us.*

How well do you know me?

Mother's Perfect Morning

I woke up at [time] ....

I was looking forward to ....

First I got dressed in my favorite ....

I made my favorite breakfast of ....

.... I put on some music while I got dressed, and

my favorite song, ... ,came on.

Then I ....

Daughter's Perfect Morning

I woke up at [time]   .

I was looking forward to   .

I got dressed in my favorite   .

I made my favorite breakfast of

                                  . I put on some music while I got

dressed, and my favorite song,   ,came on.

Then I   .

Creative writing

Take turns as you write a story based on each title below and on the following pages. Daughter writes the first sentence of the story, and Mom writes the next (or vice versa). See how long you can keep it going!

Alternatively: Take turns writing a one-sentence story for each. Got extra space? Make up some of your own!

Take this Job and Love It! My Dream Job

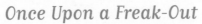

Once Upon a Freak-Out

The Monster Under My Bed

Littlest Women

The Day I Forgot My Phone

If I Were President

If I Were a Magician

That Night in the Forest

What "Girl Power" Means to Me

How I'd Spend Two Extra Hours a Day

MOTHER

Mother's turn...What I like about you, Daughter!

Daughter's turn... What I like about you, Mother!

Family history for my daughter

The Story of My Parents (Your Grandparents):

....

....

....

....

....

....

The Story of How Your Parents Met:

....

....

....

....

....

....

....

....

The Story of Your Arrival:

....

....

....

....

....

....

....

....

....

The Story of How You Were Named:

....

....

....

....

....

....

....

....

Family tales for my mother

The Story of What I Know about My Heritage:

....

....

....

....

....

....

....

....

....

....

The Story of My Earliest Memories:

....

....

....

....

....

....

....

....

....

....

The Story of Me and My Grandparents:

....

....

....

....

....

....

....

....

A Story about Me You Never Heard Before:

....

....

....

....

....

....

....

....

It's Our Time

Let's make a pact to do one special thing together every month— just the two of us.

50 starter ideas

(Borrow away! —Paula and Page)

- Before-school breakfast
- Around-the-world dinners: Different cuisine every month
- Matinee movie—or the really late show
- Girls' movie night at home, with popcorn or candy
- Mother-daughter book club for two
- Sample a different ice cream parlor every month
- Shopping spree: $_____ (fill in amount) for each of you to spend that day
- Get your nails done
- Bake something ambitious
- Go apple picking (or pick other in-season fruit)
- Binge-watch a whole TV series
- Enter a running (or walk/run) race
- Take a class together
- Vintage clothing/thrift shopping
- Play sightseers in your own town
- Volunteer at a soup kitchen
- Drive somewhere you've never been
- Afternoon at a public pool or beach
- Cosmetic counter makeovers
- Go to a flea market
- Go to a concert (take turns choosing music)
- Start one of those crazy 1,000-piece puzzles
- Play some tennis (or table tennis or badminton)
- Library day

- Museum day
- Feed the ducks at the park
- Visit the zoo
- Teach yourselves to knit
- Play video games
- Compare pastries at different bakeries every month
- Hit an amusement park
- Go horseback riding
- Go bicycling
- Watch the sunrise or sunset
- Go to tag sales looking for a certain kind of item
- Go window shopping
- Overnight weekend at a B&B
- Take a hike somewhere cool; pack a picnic
- Learn a recipe neither of you have ever made
- Go to a pro sports game
- Record each other's oral histories
- Tie-dye T-shirts
- Find an outdoor café and pretend you're in Paris
- Learn origami (or try another craft)
- Plant a garden, or add to it
- Take portraits of one another
- Meet another mother-daughter duo you like for tea
- Art Day–go to the park and sketch or paint
- I Pick Day
- You Pick Day

Collaborate:

Brainstorm ideas together!

Something we could cook together:

....

....

....

....

Something we could bake together:

....

....

....

....

Places to go for sweets:

....

....

....

....

Places to go for a day trip:

....

....

....

....

Places to go for breakfast:

Classes we could take together:

A great place to take a walk:

Mom's favorite stores:

Daughter's favorite stores:

....

....

....

....

....

....

Causes we could champion:

....

....

....

....

....

....

Any rules for "our time"?

....

....

....

....

....

....

Good day of the month to aim for:

....

What we did
Our fill-in record

Definites for this year

January

February

March

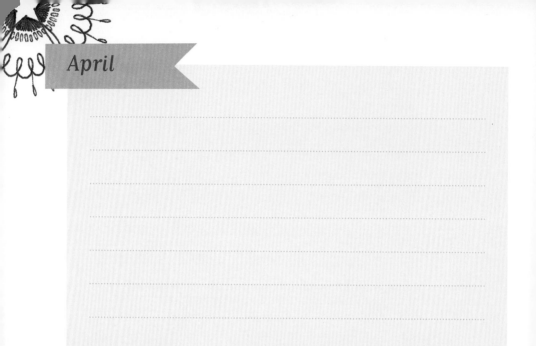

April

May

June

July

August

September

October

November

December

Some ideas for next year!

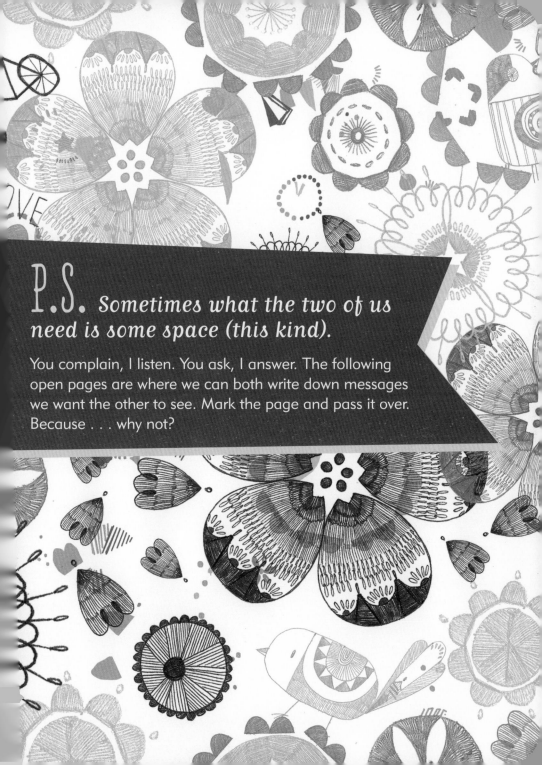

P.S. Sometimes what the two of us need is some space (this kind).

You complain, I listen. You ask, I answer. The following open pages are where we can both write down messages we want the other to see. Mark the page and pass it over. Because . . . why not?

QUESTIONS

QUESTIONS

BAD MOOD PAGES

BAD MOOD PAGES

GRATITUDE PAGES

GRATITUDE PAGES

CELEBRATIONS

CELEBRATIONS

COMPLAINTS, INJUSTICES, ANNOYANCES, AND PETTY GRIEVANCES

COMPLAINTS, INJUSTICES, ANNOYANCES, AND PETTY GRIEVANCES

WEIRD DREAMS I HAD TO SHARE

WEIRD DREAMS I HAD TO SHARE

RANDOM MISCELLANEOUS PAGES

About the Authors

Paula Spencer Scott *is the author of* The Pregnancy Journal *(Peter Pauper Press),* Momfidence *(Three Rivers Press), and* Surviving Alzheimer's *(Eva-Birch Media), as well as a co-author of* The Happiest Toddler on the Block *(Bantam), among other books. A former columnist for* Woman's Day *and* Parenting *magazines, she and her husband have six kids. This is her daughter* **Page Spencer**'s *first book. They live in the San Francisco Bay area.*